Pooems

A humorous anthology of animal poo

by Nicola Winsland

Introduction

I bet you never thought you'd one day find yourself thumbing through the pages of a little book containing a collection of poems about poo! Well, believe me... it never crossed my mind that I'd ever write such a collection, but nonetheless here it is!

Although I hear the poo word being bandied about pretty much every day by the children I support as an Early Years practitioner, the idea for my little book has come from the brilliant National Poo Museum, which opened its doors to the public on 25th March 2016. Located in the bowels of a 19th century fort on the Isle of Wight, this fun and informative exhibition dedicated to all things poo, has become an instant success, and just as it has aroused the curiosity and fascination of folks right across the globe, it has inspired me to put pen to paper and write pooetry!

Whilst this little book is full of fun and humour, there is of course a serious side to poo. For instance, poo can tell us a great deal about an animal's health and well-being, and scientists within the Zoo and veterinary community rely heavily on poo for their research purposes.

The rest of the time though, poo can be just plain funny, and little children everywhere cannot resist the temptation to shoehorn a bit of toilet humour into their everyday vocabulary and conversations!

I had enormous fun writing my pooems... I sincerely hope you have as much fun reading them.

Nicola Winsland

Pooems

A humorous anthology of animal poo

Contents

The Poo who's who

Cow poo

This sloppy brown enormous splat,
When dried would make a splendid hat.
But when it's fresh you'll have a fit,
Should you put your foot in it!

"I'm thinking some sort of floppy sun hat for this one"

"My word they really do look like olives"

Goat poo

Shiny black not hard to spot,
They look like olives but they're not.
Where they poo it matters not...
'cause mostly goats don't give a jot.

Horse poo

Like falling apples, see them tumble,
These windfalls aren't meant for your crumble.
Leave them be, and let them harden,
Then spread them all around your garden.

"There ain't no crumble good enough for my horsey apples!"

Sea Gull poo

To squirt his poo is a gull's compulsion,
And it looks exactly like emulsion.
The upshot is that you will faint,
When you find out it isn't paint!

"Well what d'you know...
I've pooped magnolia!"

"Phew! Even
I'm offended"

Pig poo

Don't stand downwind of piggies poo,
For the smell of it will offend you.
At arms length it is best you stay,
And fan the smell the other way.

"I mean... as if I could
do a smelly poo!"

Dog poo

Now this poo causes so much stress.
We're talking here about dog mess!
Of all the different kinds of poos...
You won't want this one on yer shoes!

Snail poo

Yes...it happens to be true
A snail really does a poo!
But to see what tiny snails pass,
You'll need a magnifying glass.

"They may be small, but they're perfectly formed"

Elephant poo

Let's move on now to the extreme,
And to a mighty poo machine!
When set on fire his dung display,
Will keep the mosquitoes at bay.

"You'd better make it snappy, someone's gone to get the matches!"

Rabbit poo

Rabbits on the other hand
Shed mini poos across the land.
They scatter currants far and wide,
And decorate the countryside.

"Tah-dah! Here's one I pooped earlier"

Zebra poo

Contrary to all the hype,
Zebras poos don't have a stripe.
So it's conceivable of course,
That you could muddle them with horse.

"D'you mind there's nothing
horsey about my poos!"

"I do apologise...
I didn't see you there!"

Giraffe poo

Now keep this fella in full sight,
As his poo falls from a great height.
If on your head some should alight,
Then your day will be turned to night!

So...when exploring far and wide,
Take this poo list as your guide.
Become a sleuth and look for clues,
Then get to know who's poos is whose.

7

The Gull

Laying out on my sun bed,
A sea gull pooped upon my head.
Before I had the chance to scream,
The thief took off with my ice cream!

"Well if it's not nailed down..."

The Pigeon

Oh! What shall we do
About the pigeon poo,
That shrouds ol' London town from here to there?
For a pigeon generally
Poos wherever he may be,
No, it's not a pigeon's job to really care.

A pigeon can't be too well bred
If he'll poop on Nelson's head,
Not to mention the Palace balcony.
A pigeon thinks it is a lark
To poo his way all round Hyde Park,
Where he stores it is a bloomin' mystery!

He'll poo on folks in Oxford Street,
All the bobbies on the beet,
A pigeon isn't noted for his pride.
Wherever you may roam,
He'll zap you before you're home.
Regrettably there's no place you can hide.

Some folks have even found
Pigeons on the underground.
Now, that's one place you would hope is sanctuary.
There are documented tales
Of pigeons pooping on the rails,
And trying to ride the carriages for free!

So what can we do
With all this pigeon poo?
Could we heat a home, or fuel a motor car?
Could somehow pigeon poo
Be turned into pigeon glue?
Then we could hail the pigeon as a superstar!

'From bot to pot!'

Let's face this poo mountain we climb,
And devote a bit of time
Dreaming up a grand idea or three.
There has to be for goodness sake,
A way that we can take
Pigeon poo and turn it into energy!

The Plight of the Dung Beetle

Dung beetle coming through
With my precious ball of poo!
Clear the decks, make way for me
I'm trying to get from A to B.

Across the desert I must go
With my ball of poo in tow.
Step aside, why can't you see,
This poo is twice the size of me!

Let me pass, or I'll be late.
I'm trying to roll a hundred weight.
Out my way 'cause honestly,
Me poor ol' legs are killing me!

Through the jungle I must go,
Why I do it I dunno.
I know that look it's plain to see
You're thinking rather you than me!

For days I roll without a rest.
I am a dung beetle possessed.
But Mother Nature tells me to
Spend my days transporting poo!

Into the wilderness I speed.
It's very arduous indeed.
Without a doubt the question begs...
How come I'm not blessed with more legs!

'Phew! And I'm not
even half way yet!'

The Mole

I know a mole is very fond of digging.
I know he can't resist a worm or two.
But there's something on my mind,
There's no trace that I can find,
Of where he likes to go to do a poo.

Does he do it on the top of a mountain?
Does he leave it at the bottom of a hill?
Has he ever just for fun
Tried to do it on the run?
Or is it in his nature to keep still?

Does he need to find a quiet and cosy corner?
Does he do it in the branches of a tree?
Does he nip behind a bush
Where it flies out in a whoosh?
Or does like to place it carefully?

Is he drawn to do a poo among the flowers?
Is he wanton of a panoramic view?
Has he ever for a laugh,
Left it up your garden path,
As a little gift for you to step into!

I know a mole can devastate your garden,
And getting him to leave is not an easy task.
But as for where he likes to poo...
Well I haven't got a clue,
And I can't remember why I thought I'd ask!

"Have that one on me!"

The Puppy

I'm trying to train my puppy to
Go outside to do his poo.
But it's somewhat of a rocky ride,
As he favours doing it inside.

He left a parcel on the stair.
My shower cap had one in there!
Plus, the pocket of me dressing gown
Harboured something strangely brown!

I dodged another three or four
Nestled on me vinyl floor!
Then I had a shock when I tried to
Slip my foot inside my shoe!

I'm shattered, as I never stop
With my bucket and me mop.
These days I've lost the will to smile,
As I scoop up pile after pile.

Yet my puppy doesn't sense I fear,
His days are numbered living here,
And now I've spied me tufted Mat...
I'm gonna swap him for a cat!

'Why poo in the grass.... when
you can poo in a tea pot!'

12

The Brother

My brother who is five
Has acquired an attitude.
He's gone from being cute
To embarrassingly rude.
It's futile me reminding him
It's not what he should do,
As he likes to poke his tongue out
And tell me I'm a poo!

Poo seems to be his favourite word.
He says it all the time.
Whilst poo may be his favourite word
It certainly isn't mine.
Before the cockerel crows
His morning cock-a-doodle-doo,
My charming little brother's told me...
I'm a stinky poo!

My brother says his clothes are poo,
His teachers and his food.
His whole world is one giant poo
When he is in a mood.
His hair is poo, his friends are poo,
And all his family,
And when he isn't talking poo...
He's on about wee wee!

My little brother's five,
But I'm counting up the days,
Until he's out the other side
Of this pooey phase.
I'm hoping when that day arrives
He'll see my point of view...
Then we can laugh about the time
When everything was poo!

"Poo! Poo! Poo! Poo!"

The Sister

Me sister may be tiny
But she makes a giant pong!
When it drifts into the garden
Folks all shout, "By heck that's strong!"
They run inside and bolt the doors,
And all the windows too,
So you wanna thank yer lucky stars...
She don't live next to you!

"Phew! She smells worse than I do!"

The Crow

"There's plenty more
where this came from!"

A crow comes in our garden.
It's not my Daddy's friend.
It poos on our car windscreen
Which drives Daddy round the bend

While Dad is out there scrubbing,
The crow is waiting there.
And when Daddy isn't looking,
It squirts poo everywhere!

Me Dad turns red with anger,
And shouts a filthy word.
The crow just sits there blinking,
And squirts another turd!

Me crimson Dad now seething
Storms off to the shed,
He comes out with a slingshot...
We know what's in his head.

Dad takes his aim and fires.
The Crow does not react.
Me Dad (way off his target,,)
Hits the neighbour's cat!

Dad then deserts the crime scene,
A cowards thing to do.
The Crow takes full advantage,
And squirts another poo!

Upsetting our poor neighbour
Isn't where this story ends,
'Cause sadly for my livid Dad,
The Crow has told his friends.

Now everyday when Daddy
Is completely out of sight,
They turn his newly polished car
From red to yucky white!

15

The Fly

It's enough to churn your spleen
knowing where a fly has been.
It's not a line of thought you should pursue.
For it's a fly's desire to eat
All that God's creatures excrete,
Yes there's only one thing on a fly's menu!

And that is.....
Cat poo,
Rat poo,
Thin poo,
Fat poo,
Poo in the extreme.
Dog poo,
Frog poo,
Hedgehog poo,
Poo that's whipped like cream.

Pig poo,
Donkey poo,
Straight poo,
Wonky poo,
Poo that's tinged with green...
Tough poo,
Rough poo,
Can't get enough poo
When you're really keen!

A fly is happy when he's found
A steaming poo pile on the ground.
He feels as if he's won the lottery.
But since he likes to stick his feet,
In what God's creatures excrete,
I'd prefer it if he didn't land on me!

"Now that's what I call a Mr Whippy!"

16

Thanks to the...
Brown poo,
White poo,
Give you half a fright poo,
Poo that has a sheen.
Matt poo,
Flat poo,
Shaped like a hat poo
Perfect for a queen.

Mouse poo,
Grouse poo,
Teeny weeny louse poo
To small to be seen...
Hare poo,
Bear poo,
I'm gonna need some air poo...
If you know what I mean!

So when you see a little fly,
You better hope he passes by,
You won't want him in the near vicinity.
But should a fly decide to stay,
Take to your heels and run away,
As you know what he's been eating recently!

The Nose

I have the kind of nose
That is sensitive to smell.
Just the whiff of something horrid
And I start to feel unwell.
I turn a shade of green,
And me legs become like jelly.
I have been known to faint
When the air is really smelly!

I loathe the smell of pasta.
I can't bear the smell of cheese.
Take away that smelly fish cake,
And those putrid smelly peas!
I won't eat that smelly jam,
Nor will I touch that smelly bread.
You can keep those smelly eggs,
It's their smelly fumes I dread!

I dislike the smell of flowers.
I detest the smell of trees.
I freak out when I smell horse manure
Floating on the breeze!
I won't pass a smelly bin,
Or put on a smelly shoe.
I won't have a smelly dog
In case he does a smelly poo!

So to solve my smelly problem,
I'm going to propose
That I take my pointy fingers
And I stick 'em up my nose!
That's where I aim to keep 'em
Until some fresh air flows,
And let's hope that I can manage
Using only my elbows!

"This could be tricky!"

18

The Pants

I love tractors.
I love rabbits.
I love kangaroos and pears.
I love monkeys.
I love snowflakes.
I love sliding down the stairs.
I love ice cream.
I love scooters.
I love cats and elephants,
But you won't believe how much I love...
The robots on my pants!

"...And I'm never taking them off!"

19

The Dinosaur

If next to you,
Fresh dino poo,
Is falling all around,
Forget your fears,
Protect your ears,
Before it hits the ground!
It's no surprise
A dino's size,
Means monstrous poos as well,
With fingers locked,
In ears now blocked,
You can't avoid the smell!

"If only I had three arms!"

The Chicken

I'm at a loss, what shall I do?
On my egg there's chicken poo!
How it got there, I can't tell,
An egg should have a spotless shell.
I also note this poo's a tether,
For a tiny chicken feather.
Now my problem is twofold,
Though some would argue I've struck gold.
Since poo and feathers are a find
Of a very welcome kind,
Throwing it would be a waste....
As chicken poo adds to the taste!

"Uh-oh! I've laid another reject!"

Nicola Winsland

Early days and influences

My first attempts at writing verse came at a very early age when I would compose funny little rhymes for friends and family to celebrate birthdays and special occasions. Inspired by traditional nursery rhymes and limericks, I enjoyed writing my own versions with a somewhat irreverent twist! I especially loved to read humorous stories with a rhyming text, and Roald Dahl, Lynley Dodd, and Colin West are still three of my favourite authors. At school when I should have been getting to grips with such things as logarithms and Sir Humphry Davy's safety lamp, my best friend and I were discretely writing outrageous adventure stories about the poor unsuspecting staff and pupils of our school.

College Days

I studied graphic design for four years at Portsmouth College of Art and Design where I discovered I wasn't a graphic designer - I was an illustrator at heart. Having had a great interest in butterflies for many years, I began painting studies of them in their natural surroundings. After leaving College I freelanced for a couple of years exhibiting my paintings and taking on commissioned work. My love of butterflies subsequently turned into my profession for almost a decade when my family and I built and ran our own butterfly farm which opened to the public in 1984.

Change of Career

After I'd married and my daughter started school, I trained as an Early Years Practitioner and I have been working with children across the Foundation Stage for the last fifteen years. For the past four years I have been writing a blog which chronicles life in my classroom through humorous stories, illustrations and rhymes totally inspired by the funny things the children say and do. I'm a passionate walker. I walk every day on the Downs where I live in Ventnor on the Isle of Wight. It is whilst walking on these beautiful downs that I conjure up my stories and poems.

Helen Ellis-Brown

I have been creatively inspired by so many things from an early age - textiles, animals, the coastline...I enjoy designing and making things and love applying my attention to the details. My first job was at a small print and design company, with no formal training, I quickly picked up the basic skills of typography and layout and fell in love with composition and making things 'work' on the printed page. Since those early days I have worked as a senior designer for brands large and small.

I met Nicola a few years ago, a college friend of my husband, and have really enjoyed developing this wonderful book with her. Nicola has a natural writing ability which combined with her beautiful illustrations has led to what I hope will be the first of many delightful books that take a light hearted approach to some of the situations we face in everyday life.